GOOD DOG, BAD DOG:
DOUBLE IDENTITY

BY DAVE SHELTON

Wait for me here, Dooley.

Police, ma'am. I won't be needing a ticket.

Well, he got away from me this time, Sweetlips, and I'm sorry about that...

...but at least you're safe now.

Thank you, Sam.

Sam, I...

Look out, Sylvia! Behind you!

McBoo!

WAAAAAAH!

Oh, hello, Bergman. What are you doing here?

Got a call about a case. Came to pick you up.

But how did you even know I was here?

Easy. I'm a detective!

Also, you'd written it in your desk diary.

Aw, can't I stay to the end? I want to see who the murderer was.

The maid did it. She's secretly in love with the gardener and getting revenge for something horrible Lady Etheridge said about his geraniums.

Wow! How can you know all that?

Like I said...

...I'm a detective!

Dooley, get us to Wiener Brothers Studios, and fast!

Yessir!

VRROOOM

RING

RING

Hello, Wiener Bros Studios, where the stars shine brightest. How can I...?

Well, hi, Rosalind. How are you today?

Ahem!

How was the party, Saturday?

No!

No?

Noooo!

Excuse me, ma'am

Well that was stupid! And in those shoes? She should know better!

Ma'am, we're police officers and if we could just...

Mildred! Mildred, have you got the figures for **The Fifty Winks** yet? I gotta meeting with...

Who the heck are **these** guys?

Detective Kirk Bergman. This is Detective Duncan McBoo.

Hullo.

You Sam Wiener?

Cops, huh? Nah, nah, Sam ain't here. He had to go out to a location shoot near Dog Leg Falls. Can I help ya?

Well, it was Mr Wiener that called so we should really talk to—

Well, I'm still **Mr** Wiener, I just ain't **Sam**. Name's Jack Wiener. Wiener **Brothers**, see? Sam and me're twins.

Now, what are you here for? I ain't got all day.

Your brother said someone's been getting some kinda threatening letters.

You know anything about that?

Sam called you about that, huh?

Well, yeah, one of our actors has been getting some kinda crank mail.

I figure it's just baloney but I hear Dunstan's pretty shook up about it.

Dunstan?

You mean Dunstan Bassett? Wow!

Is this guy meant to be famous, then?

What?! But you must have seen his movies! Haven't you seen **Lying Doggo**?

Or **Bite Club**?

Or **The Longest Walk**?

Dunstan Bassett's a **star!** A real dog's dog!

He's a **hero!**

Heh! Yeah, sure.

Hey, Mildred, hold my calls. I'm taking these fellas to Lot 19.

Come and meet Dunstan for yourselves, fellas!

About these letters, Wiener: you know of anyone who might want to cause Bassett harm?

Dunstan? Nah! Everybody loves Dunstan.

It's like your pal here says: he's a hero.

At least on screen he is.

Nah. I tell ya, those letters ain't serious.

All our stars get some kinda crazy mail once in a while. It goes with the territory.

Bassett's just getting old and jumpy. Pat him on the head and tell him it'll all be okay and he'll be fine.

Heck, Wiener, you don't think we have better things to—

Better be quiet, fellas. They're filming.

Righto, Mr Wiener. Tippy toes it is.

Quiet on set!

ACTION!

Okay, Wiener. We'll give the letters the once over, tell your guy not to worry and scoot.

But I'm not happy!

No offence, detective, but you don't exactly strike me as the happy type anyway!

I just want some real work to do, Wiener!

?!

Real work on a real ...

...case!

BOOM

Ah!

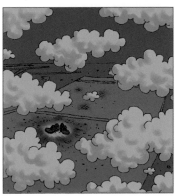

McBoo, are you okay?

Aye, I think so.

How about you, Bergman. Are you dead?

No, McBoo, not this time.

Just as well. We've certainly got a real case to work on now!

Heh! You figure?

Oh, Mr Bassett!

Do you think he's all right?

I'm guessing not, McBoo!

Aw, that's a shame!

I was hoping I could get his autograph.

Dunstan! Oh, what a tragedy! Such a great talent cruelly stolen from us!

Such a loss! Such a terrible loss!

Hmm...

Say, Ada! You got that on film, right?

Sure, Jack, but...

Great! We can sell the footage to the newsreel companies!

And when the movie's finished, we can sell it to the public as a tribute. They'll lap it up!

Yeah, yeah, we'll make a killing!

Someone already did, Jack!

What? Oh Dunstan? Don't worry about him! We had him insured up the wazoo!

Heck, we'll make as much from that as from the movie!

Ah, you're all heart, Jack!

But, sorry to break it to you: Dunstan's not dead!

What?

The old ham said he was too spooked by those letters to do any work. He's been hiding in his dressing room all day.

But then who...

Bump Henderson was standing in for him. No dialogue and shot from behind, I figured we could get away with it.

Henderson? Oh, the stunt guy?

Yeah, poor old Bump. He—

Yeah, yeah. We'll send flowers to his mother.

Now get back to work!

If we ain't cashing in on Bassett kicking the bucket then I need you to bring this picture in on time and under budget!

So I want this place cleaned up, pronto, and...

...everyone back to work!

Uh?

Hey!

I'm afraid we can't let you do that, Mr Wiener.

This is my darn studio, buster, and I'll do what I—

It's not a studio any more! It's a crime scene now!

And that puts us in charge!

Let's get you outside for a breath of fresh air, Mr Wiener. You're looking a bit hot and bothered!

You don't like him much, do you?

Nope, can't say that I do.

You got taste, mister!

Ada Volpino, director. Pleased to meetya.

Ah, I need to talk to you.

Everybody else, get out of our way!

McBoo, collect some samples for the lab willya?

Righto, Bergman.

So, Miss Volpino: looks like someone tried to blow up your lead actor.

Any idea who'd want to do that?

Have you **seen** any of his movies lately?

Not so good, huh?

Nah! Dunstan was a big noise back in the day, but his last few movies were, well...

...bombs!

But I don't know who'd want to kill him. I figure most people think he's dead already!

His career certainly is!

9

Tum te tum te tum...

Hmm...

sniff sniff

Ech!

Could you not afford soap on a stuntman's wages, Bump Henderson?

Ooh, now...

...what's this here?

Oh, goody. Costumes!

It won't hurt just to try on one or two...

Ooh, yes - I hear the deckchair look is very big this season...

creak squeak

?

Is there somebody there?

!

CLUNK

That'll be a yes, then.

...And the film you shot of the explosion - we'll need to see that.

Sure, we'll get it processed overnight, like usual. You can see it...

...um...

...in the morning.

Uh?

What's going on?

Bergman...

Well, I'm not sure but...

...I think your partner wants some help catching that mysterious stranger in a top hat.

...could you give me a hand catching this mysterious stranger in a top hat, please?

Oop!

twang

Eek!

Look out!

OOF!

WHUMP

CRASH

Excuse me, Miss Volpino.

Uh...that's okay.

No time for lying around, Bergman! There's chasing to be done!

Good.

I like chasing.

There's no use running, mister!

You won't get away you kn—

OH!

Ooh!

Ah!

Darn it!

Ow!

No sign of him. He's got away!

Oh bother!

And it's all your fault!

You know it's a serious business obstructing the police, mister!

Police? Oh, you're the detectives!

I was just on my way to find you.

My name's Able. I'm the, um, head of security for Wiener Bros.

Jack told me to bring you these.

Shortly...

KNOCK
KNOCK

Oh!

H-hang on a moment.

Y-yes?

Who is it?

Police, Mr Bassett! Open up!

Is this about those dreadful letters? Oh, thank goodness. I had begun to wonder if anyone would ever take them seriously.

Well, we usually take it pretty seriously when someone gets blown up!

Blown up! Oh good gracious? Who...?

Your stunt double, Bump Henderson.

You mean you hadn't heard?

With those ears?

Hmf! No. No, I hadn't... Um... What...?

Time bomb in a grandfather clock. Nasty!

Oh my!

Any idea who might be sending these, Bassett?

Um... no, I'm afraid not.

It's not as if I have any real enemies.

At least, I didn't think so.

Well, these aren't exactly friendly, mister!

You Will die DUNstAn BasSETt! XXX

No. And they've got worse! The more recent ones don't even have kisses on the bottom!

Well, they don't give us any obvious leads, but maybe the lab boys can do something with them.

Oh, and you ought to know that someone fled the scene of the crime earlier and is still at large.

We don't know for sure that he's the killer...

...but if he is then I'm sure Mr Able will look after you.

Oh, and just one more thing, Mr Bassett.

Can I have your autograph?

13

Gimme coffee!

Geez, Mr Bergman, you look **terrible**!

Why, thank you, Harry. Now pour, willya!

We interviewed thirty witnesses yesterday. Then we were up half the night typing up their... **slurp**...

...statements. Then we were up most of the other half of the night reading and rereading those statements...

...and finding absolutely nothing in any of them of any darn use to us!

I've had one hour's shut eye. I'm entitled to look a little rough!

Keep it comin'!

You want somethin' to eat with that?

Nah, solids just slow down the effect. Anyway, as soon as McBoo gets here we'll be straight back to it.

McBoo? He got here an hour ago. Had the greedy gutbuster breakfast special.

Then another.

And now puddings.

Y'know that boy's not so much a customer as a whole **career**!

Oh yeah, he's got a talent for eating all right!

Say, gimme that, willya?

Hey!

SNATCH

gulp gulp gulp

ZOINK

That's more like it! Now let's get this show on the road!

Come on, McBoo! Let's see if there's any news for us at the lab.

The lab? Brilliant!

Can I feed the guinea pigs?

Uh, I guess so.

But no juggling this time, okay?

One time I did that and now no one will let me forget it.

Well, it was a memorable sight, McBoo.

Sadly.

Hello, Dr Ince.

Ah, Mr Bergman...

...pff...

...just a moment.

Hullo, Dr Ince. Lovely to see you again.

McBoo?!

Don't drink that!

Oh. Okay.

How... nice... to see you back again. Please, have a seat.

Sit very still.

Don't touch — or eat — anything.

Now, Mr Bergman...

These letters you gave me to look at — they don't give much away, I'm afraid

Obviously we've no handwriting to analyse: the text is written with these cutout letters and the addresses on the envelopes are typed.

Postmarks are from all over. Never the same twice.

The paper and the envelopes, on the other paw, are always the same. Extremely common brands, so no help to us.

And the cutout letters come only from mainstream newspapers with high circulations.

Screening room 2, Wiener Bros Studios.

Ooh, comfy seats! Lovely!

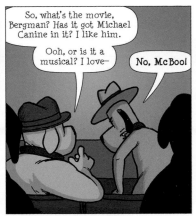

So, what's the movie, Bergman? Has it got Michael Canine in it? I like him.

Ooh, or is it a musical? I love—

No, McBool

We're here to see the footage they shot yesterday.

Oh, yes, of course. The film of the explosion.

No songs, then?

No, McBoo.

Just watch it carefully for any clues. And the cast and crew here too, see how they react. Someone might give themselves...

Is that popcorn?

Um... yes.

We're about to watch Bump Henderson blown to pieces... and you brought popcorn?

Er... yes.

Where did you even get that?

I had it in the car. It's my emergency popcorn.

You have emergency popcorn?

Oh, aye, of course. I have emergency a lot of things.

You can't be too careful.

Oh, look, here's Miss Volpino.

Is everyone here?

Yeah, yeah! Now get on with it, Dollface, willya? Time is money, ya know!

What about Sam?

Aw, he's not comin'. He's at home with a cold in the head. Don't sweat it though, I'm keepin' him informed.

Okay, Jack.

Well, everyone, I know you must all be feeling the terrible loss of our good friend, Bump Henderson.

But if you knew Bump at all well then you'll know that he wouldn't want us to make any fuss.

17

He wasn't a sentimental kind of guy. And he never felt sorry for himself so he wouldn't want us to feel sorry for him.

He'd want us to carry on.

So that's why we're showing the "dailies" as usual today. In tribute to a great stunt dog and—

GET ON WITH IT!

Yeah, thanks a lot, Jack. Okay, well...

...ah, roll the film please, Leonard.

Here we go, McBoo. Eyes peeled, okay?

Okay, Bergman!

Hello again, Detective.

Miss Volpino.

Baskerville Hall, Bump Henderson make-up test.

CLACK

So, whaddya reckon, ladies? Do I look like a movie star?

Ha! Not yet, Bump, but we'll see what we can do.

Are you ready for your ears now, Mr Henderson?

Sure thing, Toots, thanks!

Ha ha... oh that tickles! Hee!

Oh, hold still, ya big galoot!

Ha, look at me, I'm Dunstan Bassett!

This all right, Miss Volpino?

Yeah, you'll do just fine, Bump!

Baskerville Hall, scene twenty-three, take one.

CLACK

B/VILLE HALL
DIR: VOLPINO
23 / 1

BOOM

Oh, poor Bump!

Sob!

Horrible! Just horrible!

Such a waste!

I just... can't believe it.

Sniff!

CRUNCH

munch munch

No respect!

Disgraceful!

Tsk!

Oh, McBoo!

Look, maybe you'd better just leave!

Kinda looks like the natives are getting restless!

I'm gonna need to watch this over a coupla times. You go see what rumours you can pick up around the place. And keep out of trouble!

Okey dokey, Bergman.

Right then, time for a bit of sneaky snooping!

Where would be a good place to do that?

Somewhere where people feel relaxed and chatty.

Hmm...

Oop! Rumblings in my tum!

I wonder where a dog could get a spot of brunch around here.

That'd keep Bergman happy.

Tch! "Keep out of trouble" he says!

As if I'm the one who gets in trouble.

19

Ahem! Hey, buddy!

Hmm? Oh, hello.

RUMBLE GRUMBLE

I don't mean to be rude or nuthin', but if your stomach gets any louder you're gonna ruin the sound on every picture we're makin' here.

ROWRRRRR

You wanna muffle the racket with some chow? I'm headed for the canteen myself if you wanna come along.

Oh, yes, please. Lead on.

Nice costume, by the way. What is it? Some kind of space rabbit?

What?

Nah!

I'm **Lobzilla**, the menace from the bottom of the sea!

I get to destroy Atlantis on Tuesday!

Nice.

So what are you working on yourself, mister? You in that cop movie they're shooting on Lot 14?

Oh, no, I'm...

Crikey! That's Nick Jackalson!

Sorry... um... what did you ask me?

What are you working on?

Oh, a murder case.

Oh, so you're a real police hound?

Aye, that's right.

Plenty of mash for you, Mr Bayfuss?

Yes, please, Muriel.

Meanwhile...

Darn it! A dozen times I've watched that film clip...

...and I can't see a single clue in it! A whole day in and still nothing to go on!

Heck, it's like we haven't even started this case yet!

So what now, Mr Detective?

Well, I guess I'll check in with the la—, see if they'e gotten anythi—, new from the letters.

Then find McBoo and question a bunch more dogs for hours and hours.

Gah!

I hate this bit! Finding out who did it. It's just so... dull!

I like it when we know who the bad guy is! I like the chase and the fight, see?

Oh yeah?

Oh yeah!

But we don't know who to chase yet.

So in the meantime...

More questioning?

Yup. 'Fraid so.

Well, if you have to, then maybe you'd better question **me!**

Say tonight, at 8.00. You know the Green Daisy Club?

Sure, but—

But me no buts, fella. I'm buying you dinner.

You saved my life yesterday. Where I come from, that earns a dog a steak!

You can question me all you like over dessert.

Now, hang on a—

Eight o'clock, Detective.

Don't be late!

So I guess you're here about that stunt guy who got blown up, huh?

Aye, that's right. Bump Henderson. Did you know him at all?

Uh, yeah, I... knew old Bump. A little.

Nice guy.

You got any idea who...?

Eh? Oh well, it seems the bomb was **actually** meant for Mr Bassett.

Bump was just unlucky to be standing in for him.

So, McBoo...

...explain to me why we're going to a **junk shop** to try to solve a **murder case**.

Well, for three reasons:

Because Hector Greenstreet, the chap that owns it, knows more about the movie business than anyone else in the city.

Because I need to buy a birthday present for my Aunt Mary.

McBoo!

ERT

But mainly because we don't have any better ideas.

We're here.

GREENSTREET'S EMPOR

Ooh, nice mirror!

Do you think I'm losing weight? I'm worried I'm getting a bit skinny!

How do you know this guy, anyway?

KNOCK KNOCK KNOCK

Sorry we are CLOSED

Oh, I arrested him about ...seven years ago. For handling stolen goods.

Great!

NOT Sorry we are CLOSED

OPENING TIMES WHENEVER DARK WI FEEL LI

KNOCK KNOCK KNOCK

The sign says **CLOSED**, mister! Now, why don't you scoot before I...

Oh, hello, McBoo. Come in.

Thanks, Hector. This is Bergman, by the way.

Pleased to meet you, Mr Bergman.

Sorry about that! I get kinda riled when my afternoon nap gets interrupted.

You know, you could get into a bunch of trouble waving guns at police officers, buddy!

Aw, I'm sorry! But, heck, this thing ain't even real!

It's just a prop from a movie.

I collect 'em, see?

Hey, you wanna see my collection? It's dynamite! Come on, come on!

Now, look here, we—

We'd love that, Hector. Thank you.

All righty, then. This way, fellas.

Here you are, boys. Whaddya think?

Wow!

Isn't that the robot from **Silent Walkies**?

Ooh, and the sarcophagus from **Cleocatra**?

Just looks like more junk to me!

Amazing!

Yeah, it is amazing, ain't it? Best collection in the city, I reckon!

So, what can I do for you, McBoo?

Oh yes! Do you know anything about Bump Henderson, Hector?

Well, I know he got blown up!

Kinda ironic, really. He worked in demolition before he got the movie bug, you know. A real explosives whizz!

But hey, if **that's** the case you're working on then you must be able to get...

Autographs? Yup! I got a bundle of them today. Here, take a look.

Lessee... Kirk Dogleash! Brad Pitbull! Wow! **And** Richard Grrr!

Oh! Oh! Oh!

Don't suppose you'd be willing to...?

flip flop flap

Sure. I'll swap you the lot for a Dunstan Bassett if you've got one.

One? I've got dozens! Dunstan loves to sign!

Oh? He wasn't keen when I asked him!

I didn't even know what some of those words he used meant!

It was really embarrassing when I asked my mum about them!

Well, it can't be easy for Dunstan these days, McBoo.

He hasn't had a decent part in **quite** a while.

And now Jack Wiener'd rather make dumb monster movies than Dunstan's kinda thing.

TO WHOM IT MAY CONCERN WITH DEEPEST LOVE DUNSTAN BASSETT

Here. One of these suit ya?

Heck, I hear there's even a new Lobzilla movie starts shootin' in a coupla weeks.

Didya see the last one, McBoo?

LOBZILLA VS UFOS FROM DRAGON 5

Oh, no, my mum won't let me see anything scary!

Well, then she's saved you from a world of pain and disappointment, my friend!

That movie stank so bad it'd make even your mother swear!

It's such a shame! Wiener Bros used ta make great movies, ya know?

Oh, aye!

Then they made bad movies, but they were bad movies that still made a ton of money!

Now they make really terrible movies that no one wants to see!

It's downright criminal!

Yeah, right!

But it's not really as criminal as blowing people up, is it?

Come on, McBoo! We've wasted enough time here.

Righto, Bergman.

Oh, but before we go, I still need to buy...

Hmm, let me see...

Ooh! Ooh! Oh yes! That's just the thing!

Could you gift wrap it for me?

Does your aunt even like crocodiles?

Of course she does! **Everyone** likes crocodiles!

Right, where to next?

Actually, I have an, um, appointment ...at the Green Daisy Club.

The Green Daisy, eh? That's a pretty swanky joint!

I'd better take you home so you can change out of your work clothes.

Thank you, ladies and gentlemen, you're **almost** too kind. But I have a high tolerance for that sort of thing so don't be shy!

My name's Les Pawson and I'll be your host for this evening here at The Green Daisy.

And isn't it nice here?

It's certainly a step up from the kind of joint I'm used to playing!

I even had to be **shown** to my dressing room. Normally I can find it by the smell!

Good evening, sir. May I take your hat?

No! Nobody touches the hat!

As you wish, sir.

Might I enquire, sir, if you are the party dining as the guest of Miss Volpino this evening?

That's right. She here?

Indeed, sir. If you'd care to follow me...

Ahem! Miss Volpino, your dining companion has arrived.

Mm? Oh, thanks, Marcel.

Well, hello there, Bergman. I almost didn't recognise you out of uniform!

Yeah, well... my partner said I needed to dress up for this joint. So I changed my collar.

Very... stylish. So, how's the case, detective?

Terrible!

Hey, buddy! Get me a bourbon, willya? No ice.

At once, sir.

Still no leads, huh?

Nope. And now we're not even sure...

Look, what can you tell me about Bump Henderson?

Bump? But why do you ask? If the bomb was really meant for Dunstan—

Most likely, yeah. But we gotta check every possibility.

What kind of a cat helps out in the garden?

A lawn **meower**!

Heh!

Is this thing on?

pok pok

Geez Louise! This guy is terrible!

He is? I don't really know about funny.

Nor does he!

Boy! You're a tough crowd!

What does a dog have to do to get a laugh around here?

You could try telling a joke! Only a funny one for a change!

Ah he can't **tell** a joke! He **is** a joke!

Hey, waiter! Another boddle!

Heh! I think someone may have had a little too much champagne!

Still not enough to make you seem funny, pal!

Ha ha!

You know, ladies and gentlemen, as a comic my gags are very precious to me.

But I'd happily spare a couple for these fellas.

So long as they were tied tight enough!

Ooh, now that's a bit more like it!

So, anyway, what was I saying?

Oh yeah, Bump. He was a real swell guy. Used to buy me a little gift at the end of every film we worked on.

Oh yeah? So he was sweet on you, you think?

Nah! At least I don't think so.

Anyway, what are you thinking? That the bomber was some kind of crazed love rival?

I gotta tell ya, I don't get that kind of attention, detective.

And even if I did, well heck, I hope my mystery admirer'd try buying me some flowers before they resorted to dynamite!

I guess you're right.

Oh! Looks like the house band are coming on.

I hear they've got a fabulous singer!

27

Now please welcome the brightest star in our twinkling firmament here at The Green Daisy. She sings breathtaking tales of love to the melody of your falling tears...

...and the rhythm of your broken heart beating.

Ladies and gentlemen, please give a big paw to the amazing, the beautiful, the one and only...

...MADAME F!

Knock 'em dead, kid!

If my voice breaks...

!

...It's not because my poor heart aches.

Er... you okay there, Detective?

Yup! Sure! Just taking a closer look at these starters.

No, I'm not blue!

And if I cry...

...It's just that smoke got in my eyes.

It's not for you!

No, you have no place in my heart, dear.

Though you did long ago, I confess.

Now I don't mind that we are apart, dear.

I really just couldn't care less!

Ready to order now, Miss Volpino? Sir?

Er, give us a moment okay, Marcel?

(So you see, sugar, you have to understand...)

These tears I cry, they must be for some other guy!

They're not for you!

They're not...

...for you.

Oh! Bergman?!

Heh!

Hello, Fifi.

So, um... you're working here now.

Yes, I work here now.

You know, Bergman, you're getting **really** good at that detective stuff.

You should take it up professionally.

Heh, yeah. So, uh... I didn't even know you could sing, Fifi.

Honey, you could fill a library with everything you don't know about me!

Who's your friend?

Oh yeah. Fifi, this is—

Ada Volpino. Pleased to meet you, **Madame**.

Pleasure's all mine, Sugar.

All mine.

I like your outfit, by the way.

Most girls with your figure wouldn't be brave enough to risk it!

Good for you.

Well that's a pretty bold look you're sporting yourself.

And tell me: are you a **natural** pink?

Oh, Sugar...

...natural's overrated!

I don't waste my time on natural!

Now, ladies, play nice willya? Fifi, why don't you join us for—

No can do, detective. I'm working here, remember? I got songs to sing.

Anything the matter here, beautiful?

Yeah, ish thish clown bothering you?

Clown?!

Heh! No, fellas. Everything's fine.

The "clown" is an old pal of mine.

And a police dog. So maybe you'd both be better off sitting back down.

It kinda looks like standing up ain't agreeing with you too well anyways!

Ah, whaddya mean? I'm steady as a rock, me!

Thash right. He'sh shteady ash a rock!

Anyone says different is liable to get a smack in the kisser!

Thash right. A kish in the shmacker!

POW!

I used ta be a pretty good boxer back in my school days.

Ya don't wanna mesh with him, buddy. Noshirree Bob!

I gotta sledgehammer punch and feet like a ballet dancer!

He'sh got feet like a shledgehammer and a punch like a ballet dansher! Yeah!

Ya seen this, beautiful? I'm a work of art I tells ya!

He'sh a byootiful work of art!

Yeah, yeah, a real masterpiece. Now go siddown and be a still life willya?

Don't you tell me what to do!

You tell 'im, Jake! Go on, take a shwing at 'im!

Aaah!

I will! Here, take... oop!

SWISH

WHAM

Gah! You'll pay for that!

GRRR!

Ada, Fifi - this might get kinda tricky.

I think we'd better...

Fifi?

Aw heck!

Oh well!

Hands off the waiting staff, sailor boy!

BOP

Sigh!

Another bottle of wine, madam?

Thank you, Marcel. And have one for yourself, on me.

Most kind, madam. You'll find the '33 is very robust...

...beautifully balanced...

...and with a strong finish!

CRACK

So who's this Volpino dame, Bergman?

She's a director for Wiener Bros. McBoo and me're working out there.

ZONK

Wiener Bros? What's...

Oh, hang on. I just need to hit someone with table five!

Back in a second.

Whuff! So, Bergman, you and Madame F...?

Fifi's an old friend.

Hey! Less of the "old"!

Sorry about all this... oop... by the way. This isn't quite how the evening was meant to turn out.

Are you kidding?

POW

I haven't enjoyed myself so much in weeks!

So what're you working on at the ...umf... studio?

Haven't you... ah... heard? It's a murder case.

Oh yeah?

Hi-yah!

Did Jack and Sam Wiener finally kill each other, then?

duck

Eh? What do you—

WHACK

8OOOOOOOOOH!

Hey! You were saying something at the club about the Wiener brothers?

Eh? Oh, yeah...

Sam Wiener used to come into the club maybe a couple times a week and we'd talk a little.

He's a nice guy. Pretty funny, and with a heap of great stories about movie stars.

But then a while back he started talking about his brother, Jack. It was the first time I'd seen him angry.

Seems like the two of them hadn't been getting along so well for quite a while. But lately things had gotten really bad.

Philistine!

Poseur!

Bungler!

Fool!

They couldn't agree about a single thing: what kind of movies to make...

Barbarian!

Snob!

...or which stars to have in them.

It got so they just **hated** each other. And you could see it was really getting to Sam. He wasn't his usual self no more.

You know, if this chart is right...

... then you really ought to cut down on red meat!

Huh, doctors! Whadda they know?

Now, what happened next with Sam?

I don't know. he's not been back in for a few days.

But what has this got to do with the case you're working on anyway?

Maybe nothing. But it **is** kinda weird that it was Sam that called us in in the first place and we haven't even met him yet!

How come?

He's been ill. According to Jack at least.

Maybe McBoo and me'd better pay him a house call.

Yeah? Well good luck with that, Sugar. I gotta scoot.

Oh, hiya, McBoo. Your pal here was just talking about you.

Ah, Madame Fifi! Comment allez-vous?

Pas si mal, McBoo.

Mais j'ai bien peur que ma mise en plis ne se remette pas!

Ah, t'en fais pas! Elle est indestructible, ta mise en plis!

T'es un amour, McBoo. A la r'voyure.

Salut, Fifi.

What?

Nuthin'.

Oh, I brought you some grapes.

Um... only I was worried they were going off so I ate them.

Thanks a lot!

Oh! You mean: "Thanks a **bunch!**"

Ha ha ha!

Hmf!

Ha ha ha!

Ha ha ...ooh! All this laughing has sent my insides a bit funny!

GRUMFF

Oop!

BURP

Oh, so that's what happened to the flowers! I shoulda figured.

Sorry, Bergman. I, uh, got a wee bit peckish earlier.

Anyway, I thought you'd want to see the report I picked up from the lab earlier.

Lemme see that!

Heck!

But this changes everything!

C'mon, McBoo!

Y'know, I'm suddenly feeling much better now!

So let's go arrest somebody!

You will try to get my best side, won't you?

Yeah, yeah. Of course, Mr Bassett.

And keep officer Dooley out of the shot.

Now, which newspaper are you from?

The Lamppost.

Ah yes, of course.

You must forgive me. I've spoken to so many reporters lately...

Yes, you must be exhausted.

Seventeen **exclusive** interviews in two days!

Oh, I only ever give exclusives, my dear.

Uh huh.

So, I hear you've just signed on to play the lead in Steven Spielbark's next movie, **Indiana Bones**?

Oh yes! I'm so excited to be working with Steven again.

Again? I didn't realise...

Oh yes, I was in the movie that made his name: **Paws**.

Admittedly only as a dead body, but I like to think I brought some magic to the part...

...that made Steven think of me for this new role.

Uh huh.

Nothing to do with all these press stories suddenly making you a hot property, then?

Well, perhaps a little.

My career **does** seem to have undergone something of a revival amid all the attention.

It's as if, from all this dreadfulness, a new world of opportunity is being born.

As if at any moment a new door might open and someone will say—

DUNSTAN BASSETT, YOU'RE UNDER ARREST!

Oh!

Now **this** is a story!

Cuff him, Dooley!

Yessir!

Oh!

Oh dear!

35

Interview room number 2, 23rd Precinct.

Why'd ya do it, Bassett?

Why'd ya kill Bump Henderson?

What? But I didn't—

Don't try to deny it!

We've had a report back from the lab on those "death threats" you received.

Oh yes, those dreadful, dreadful letters...

Well, you should know, Bassett...

...after all, you sent them!

Da da DAAAAAH!

McBool

Sorry. I thought, you know, that was a bit... dramatic...

I'll just shut up for a bit, shall I?

Ahem... you used spirit gum on that first letter. Kinda glue that actors use to stick on false beards and such.

Like you had in your dressing room.

But that doesn't prove—

No. No it doesn't. But this does: on the back of some of the bits of newspaper you used were parts of a crossword.

The ink and the handwriting match perfectly this autograph of yours.

Oh!

TO WHOM IT MAY CONCERN WITH DEEPEST LOVE Damien Bassett

Well, yes. All right. I did send myself the letters.

But you can't seriously believe I had anything to do with the bomb.

I just wanted to be noticed again.

I just wanted a little attention.

But I wouldn't hurt anyone for it.

I'm a silly old dog, Mr Bergman.

I'm foolish and I'm vain.

But I'm no killer.

KNOCK KNOCK

Excuse me, sir. A Mr Able here to see you.

Able? Oh, yeah, the security guy from the studio.

Hello there, Mr Bergman. I heard you had Dunstan here.

What seems to be the trouble?

Trouble?

The trouble is, I believe Bassett when he says he's not a murderer.

36

Oh, well that's good. If you're finished with him then I'll drive him back to the studio.

Nah, you can't do that. We're still gonna charge him with wasting police time.

Lock him up, Dooley!

Oh dear. I'm afraid Mr Wiener won't be very pleased about that.

Well he can tell us so himself. We're gonna pay him a little visit, right now.

Hmf!

RING

I said no calls, Dolores! As in "do not dis—"

Ah heck! Well, I guess you better send them...

...in. Hello, Jack. How's your brother?

Sam? He's still ill. But what...?

We just figured out who sent the letters to Dunstan. Seeing as it was Sam called us in to investigate we should really go tell him.

Where's he live?

Oh, he ain't at home

He's out at our hunting lodge.

It's in the middle of nowhere. But if you really wanna go there, I'll draw ya a map.

McBoo, I don't know what you're doing...

...but I really hope you'll have stopped by the time I turn around.

Ya know, ya might wanna leave this till the morning.

Some of these roads are kinda tricky at night.

Thanks, but we'll take our chances!

Okay, let's take a look at this map.

North road out of town, McBoo...

...and then head towards that storm!

37

Are you **sure** this is the right way, Bergman? Only this seems like a really **peculiar** route we're taking.

Well, Jack did say it was in the middle of nowhere.

And I'm only telling you what it says on this map he drew.

Righto. Only we **have** passed that old barn three times now.

No! We've passed three different old barns.

They just all looked... quite similar.

And all had signs saying Old Jim's Barn outside.

Yeah, well, maybe Old Jim just **really** likes barns!

Maybe I should take a look at it. I was a pup scout you know. I got my mapreading badge and everything!

You keep your eyes on the road!

I can read a map perfectly well – even one as bad as this – without any help from you, buster.

I'll get us there, don't you worry!

See! There's the turning up ahead now!

I don't think that's it.

Yes it is! Off to the left there!

Are you sure?

Of course I'm sure! Don't miss it! Turn!

Well, okay, then. But don't blame—

For goodness' sake, McBoo! Can't you just—

Oh!

Ah!

FWUMF

BANG

CRASH

OW!

Much, much later...

Ooh, there it is. Isn't it cute?

I don't care. I just want it to be dry and have Sam Wiener inside it!

Cooee! Anybody home?

Sam Wiener? You there?

This is the police!

Mmf?

Whassat?

Who's...?

Ah! Quit blinding me with that flashlight, willya?

Oop. Sorry.

Mr Wiener, we're...

Don't do scary faces, McBoo!

Righto.

Detectives McBoo and Bergman, Mr Wiener.

Sorry for arriving unannounced.

That's quite all right.

But you'll have to excuse me not getting up, gentlemen.

I'm afraid I'm really not in the best of health.

But, please, find something to sit on and tell me why you're here.

Well, it's like this...

...we're mostly here to check you're still alive!

Well...

sniff

...this wretched cold is a nuisance but I hardly think it's life-threatening!

Ha! No, but a mutual friend of ours told me that you and your brother had been fighting.

And as we hadn't ever seen you at the studios, I kinda got to wondering...

You thought Jack might have killed me?

Ha! Oh that's priceless, detective!

It's certainly true that Jack and I have our differences...

...but, as you can see, he ain't killed me yet!

And even if he tried, you could soon see him off with this, eh, Mr Wiener?

Pow!

Pow!

Hey! Careful with that, buddy. That thing's loaded, you know!

Oh, don't worry, Mr W. I know what I'm...

BANG

...doing.

Oops!

Um... do you have a bucket around here anywhere? Only your roof is leaking.

Come on, McBoo. I think maybe it's time we left.

Okey dokey, Bergman.

Oh, can we give you a ride back to town, Mr Wiener?

Only, it's awfully draughty in here...

...now.

Um, after we've got our car out of the ditch, that is.

And some of the ditch out of our car.

Scratch Scratch

Uh, no... no, thanks.

I like it here. It's very peaceful. Usually.

Well, okay. If anything new comes up in the case we'll stop by and let you know.

Oh, er, no need. Just keep Jack informed. He can let me know when I get back.

Okay, then. Let's get going, McBoo.

With a little luck we may still just about get an hour or so's sleep tonight.

Right you are, Bergman.

I *think* we've got enough petrol...

It's only right we should get a little something in return.

Sure.

Say, is that gravestone made from papier mache?

Well, of course it is!

It's a movie prop. It's make believe.

But, y'see, Bump lived and died in a world of make believe! So we're burying him in a world of make believe!

It's what he would have wanted!

I think what he would have wanted was not to get blown up!

Well, yeah, sure. In an ideal world...

Anyway, he won't be here long.

We start shooting the new James Bone movie on this set in a coupla days.

...and we commit his body to the ground. Earth to earth...

...ashes to ashes...

...dust to dust.

Hey, look, McBoo. It's your lobster pal from the canteen.

Oh, yes! I wondered if he might show up.

Hello there! Nice to see you again!

You know, there's something I've been wanting to ask you.

Oh, uh, yes?

How come you're dressed up for a Lobzilla movie...

...when my pal Hector tells me they don't start filming it for another two weeks?

WHACK

Bergman!

Yes, McBoo?

CHASE THE LOBSTER!

43

45

45

46

So you say this guy is a suspect in a murder case?

WEEOOW
VROOOM

Not a suspect, no.

He's the victim.

Huh?

But he's alive! How can he be...?

Well, Doc, you just keep him that way...

...and I'll be happy to ask him.

Will he be okay, Doctor?

It's too soon to say for sure.

But he's in better shape than I would've expected after that kind of a fall.

Well he is a stuntdog. He must know all about falling.

And I think the padding in the costume must have absorbed some of the impact.

I guess so.

Say, what's he meant to be, anyways? Some kinda space rabbit?

It's gonna be a while before you can talk to him, fellas.

Why don't you wait in the diner over the street? I'll come get you if he comes round.

Come on, Bergman, let's go! Doctor's orders!

Here y'go, fellas.

Y'know, McBoo, I'm sick of this case!

Oh aye? Why's that?

BUZZZZZ..z

Because it won't...

...darn this wretched fly!

BUZZZZ

...keep still!

First, it's about threatening letters, only they turn out to be phoney.

Then it turns into a murder case, only we can't find any suspects.

And now it turns out our victim isn't even dead!

BUZZZZZZZZz.z

47

I'm not even sure...

GAH!

...that there's still a crime to investigate!

Unless we charge Henderson with wasting police time by not being dead.

I can't stand all this twisting and turning!

Why can't it just...

...keep...

...still?

THWACK
THWACK

Oh, it'll all sort itself out soon enough, Bergman.

We just need to be patient...

...and we're sure to...

Yum!

...get a hold of things.

clink

Detectives!

He's awake!

Now, you need to bear in mind: we've given him something for the pain.

He may be a little... woozy.

Okay, Doc. No problem. We'll be gentle with him.

Okay, Henderson, so tell me...

...how come you're alive?

Ha! Yeah. It was ...neat stunt, wasn't it?

I'd put... smoke bomb in... clock.

Gave me... few seconds to get... clear. and hide from... camera before...

...main charge went off.

Only problem... in confusion... turned wrong way. Instead of... getting out had to... hide in costume store.

So you faked your own death.

Why?

Someone tried to ...kill me.

But they... messed it up.

Figured they wouldn't... try again if... thought already dead.

After all... you can't kill a dead dog.

But I don't get it: you convince everyone you're dead...

... why stick around dressed up like seafood?

Just wanted... to keep eye on Ms Volpino. Make sure... safe.

Ada? Why would she be at risk?

Thought maybe... all something to do... with present.

Present? What present?

Was gonna clean it up... first, of course...

...then give it to—

ACK!

URGH!

Oh, *don't* do that!

Hkk!

Bergman, he's dead!

Poison in his water.

Oh.

But at least we've got a murder to investigate again.

Let's see... Number 51.

I guess that this must be the place.

Apartment 2A ...must be up the stairs.

And who, may I ask, might you be?

Police, mister.

Ach! You're here about Mr Henderson, I suppose.

Well, you took your time!

It was **yesterday** my wife phoned you to complain.

Such **noise** then! You would not believe! But today: not a peep!

Noise?

Yes! All that **crashing about!** What was he doing in there? Practising his stunts maybe?

Ha!

And before he always seemed such a quiet fellow.

You tell him, officer—

Mister...

...we're not actually here about Mr Henderson's noisiness...

...but I can assure you that he'll be quiet from now on!

Ah! Handy!

Sounds like someone beat us to it, McBoo.

Aye.

Looks that way too!

This is even messier than my room at home!

Darn it! Not much chance of us finding the "present" Bump mentioned now!

Aye, I suppose not. But we may as well take a look around now that we're here, eh?

You take this room, I'll investigate the kitchen.

I guess so. But it'll just be another dead end.

There'll be nothing here. Same as the lab boys got nothing from the glass he drank the poison from.

Hmm... for a rough tough stuntdog, Bump Henderson sure had a lot of romantic novels!

I don't know how anyone can read this trash!

Gasp! Lydia! You can't marry Lord Flintheart!

Poor George!

Sniff.

Ahem, anything in there, McBoo?

Plenty of evidence that he didn't like washing up!

But nothing useful, no.

I'll just, um, check the fridge...

Okay. I'll try the bedroom and then—

KNOCK KNOCK

What if that's the killer?

Did you bring your gun?

No. Did you?

Nope.

I'll find something heavy. You answer the door.

Right.

KNOCK KNOCK

Hullo, Mr Henderson?

Actually—

I'm afraid this parcel you mailed has been returned as "address unknown".

Oh, uh, thanks.

Sign here.

You can put the vacuum cleaner down now, McBoo.

Thank goodness! My arms hurt!

♪

Okay then, let's take a look at what we've got here...

That's odd! Muttley Drive? There's no such place!

Lucas Wagg 777 Muttropolis MS 20123

Why'd Bump send a parcel to somewhere that doesn't exist?

And to some**one** who doesn't exist.

Lucas Wagg is a character in an old Brad Pitbull movie!

When he needed to hide something important from the bad guys...

...he mailed it to a dreamt up address so it'd be safely caught up in the postal system for a few days...

...before being returned to sender.

CRIKEY!

It's a Sammy!

A Sammy?

You know, the movie award.

SCREEN ARTS of MUTTROPOLIS BEST PICTURE 1936

And look: this one has dried blood on it!

I think that must make it some kind of clue.

You figure?

Come on, let's get this to the station and see what the lab boys can tell us about it.

You know, Bergman, I think it really must be a pretty good sort of a clue.

Otherwise the fella in the car behind wouldn't be bothering to follow us!

ZOOM

Oh, I beg your pardon. He's not trying to follow us after all.

HE'S TRYING TO KILL US!

CRASH

Oooh! Don't hit the nun. Don't hit the nun. Don't hit the nun.

SCREEE

Oops!

WAAAAH!

CRASH

AAAAAAH!

WOOOOOH!

SMASH

Dear oh dear! Such a mess!

Time to tidy up!

Let's see now. You first. And then your friend over in the bushes.

Oh! Oh no! Where...?

Put the gun down, mister...

...I'm armed!

CLANG

54

Oh no. No, Jack didn't **hurt** anybody.

He **killed** him!

Killed? Who did he kill?

Why, his brother, of course!

You're saying Jack killed Sam Wiener? Last week?

That's what I'm saying.

Tch!

Come on, McBoo.

So it's cut and dried: Jack Wiener's your man!

Except his brother **isn't** dead! We spoke with Sam Wiener just last night!

We'll let Able stew in a cell for a while and try again later.

We're hoping he'll be more helpful after a bit of a rest.

Once he's feeling less "exhausted".

Oh, hi, McBoo. You wanna sit in for a few hands while I make some coffee?

Ooh, yes please.

Have you played poker before, McBoo?

Oh, no, not really. But I saw it in a movie once.

I'm sure I'll soon get the hang of it. You're playing for treats are you?

Heh heh!

Yeah, McBoo. Treats. Yeah.

Oh, Bergman, I took a look at those papers from Mr Able's car.

Oh yeah? Anything interesting?

Well, there were some very odd sums in the accounts books!

It looks as if Wiener Bros is in big trouble, but someone's trying to hide the fact.

And some legal documents and letters.

Looks as if Jack wants Sam to sign over control of the studios to him.

I can't see Sam agreeing to that!

Betting's all done. What you got boys?

Pair of tens.

Gah! Pair of nines.

Hah! Well I got you both beat!

Two pairs: queens and fours.

McBoo?

Snap!

McBoo! We're playing poker, not—

No, I mean snap! I've got the same: two pairs: queens and fours.

Exactly the same except for one small difference: my other card's a king and yours is a two. So I think that means... I win!

Hey Bergman, have you seen this?

What's that?

Something about your pal Jack Wiener getting some prize at the Sammy awards tonight.

TTROPOLIS HERALD

STUDIO STAND IN: Jack Wiener to accept Sammy for ill brother Sam.

Oh, that's nice. Jack's never won a movie award before.

Eh? But his office is full of them!

Oh no. They're all sporting trophies. And I'm not even sure they were really all his!

Here y'go, Bergman. Cup of... oops!

Hey, watch it! You've spilled coffee on...

Oh!

"Exactly the same except for one small difference!"

A bit of colour round his eye...

...am Wiener

Jack Wiener

And that girl at the funeral said some make-up had been stolen...

We **didn't** see Sam at the cabin. It was Jack all along!

That's why he sent us there by such a stupid route.

So he could go straight there and arrive before us.

CLONK

But not by much. We thought he had a fever but maybe—

He was sweating because he'd had to run to the cabin from his car...

WANTED DEAD, ALIVE OR POORLY.

Which he must have hidden somewhere away from the cabin so we wouldn't see it!

It all fits!

C'mon, McBoo. Let's go award Jack Wiener... a nice long prison sentence!

SCREEN ARTS OF MUTTROPOLIS
22TH ANNUAL AWARD CEREMONY

Not now, McBoo!

"A hungry detective is a bad detective"... ...that's what my old boss used to say.

SQUIT

At least I think that's what he said. It was a bit hard to tell with his mouth so full of cake.

Can I help—

Police, mister! Where's Jack Wiener?

He's in there. Table three. Front and centre.

Wow!

But he'll be up on stage soon to pick up his brother's award.

Come backstage and you can talk to him there in peace when he gets off.

It's none of my business...

...but I do hope you'll be arresting Jack for something serious.

I've never liked him.

Two minutes, Mrs Collie.

Thanks, Harry.

Well hello, handsome! And who might you be?

Oh!

Angelina Collie!

I... ah... um...

I'm Duncan McBoo and I'm very pleased to meet you.

Would you like some of my burger?

Uh, no... no thanks.

And to present our next award we have a very special guest.

The star of **Lara Crufts: Tomb Raider** - Angelina Collie, ladies and gentlemen.

Gotta go. Catch you later, boys.

You offered her some of your burger?

Well I wasn't going to give her **all** of it, was I?

59

...a special lifetime achievement award to that great dog of the movies, beloved by us all: Sam Weiner!

But Sam's sadly too ill to be here tonight so here's the other Wiener brother, Jack, to accept it on his behalf.

clap clap clap clap clap clap clap clap clap clap clap clap clap clap

Ladies and gentlemen - and the rest of you - thank you.

Sam's real sorry he can't be here tonight, but, hey, he's got enough of these things already.

At least this way I get my paws on one just for... uh...

Oh!

Oh no!

Hey!

Hands off, little brother!

I don't want your grubby paw marks all over **my** trophies!

Go play with your own.

Oh, but I forgot. You haven't got any, have you?

Ah, can it, Sam! You've got plenty of ornaments to polish, sure...

...but who made our biggest hits? **Iceberg vs Boat, Lord of the Fangs, Mrs Doubtfur** - all mine!

Oh, sure. But you made all our worst flops too.

You've lost us a lot of money the last coupla years, Jack.

Maybe it's time you quit.

Me? I'm the one guy who could **save** us?

You're the one that's gotta **go**, Sam.

In fact I've already had the papers drawn up.

Why don't ya just sign here and let me run the studio alone?

You can go spend more time fishing out at the lodge...

Never! I'll never let you take the studio from me!

68

You shot my hat!

BANG

You really shouldn't have done that!

KAPOW

Well, at least Jack got that **big hit** he wanted!

Nice work, Bergman.

Here's your hat.

Thanks.

Hey, Bergman—I think they like us!

Well, the feeling ain't mutual. Let's get out of here, McBoo!

A few weeks later...

Ah, detectives, Chief—so glad you could make it.

Good of you to invite us, Miss Volpino.

PREVIEW
TONIGHT
8·30

Oh, it's the least I could do. Since you locked up Jack, the studio has been a much nicer place to work at.

Besides, this is a film you really need to see.

How come?

Oh, didn't the Chief explain?

Oh, no. I just ordered him to come.

Oh, well, you see, when you two chased Bump through—

...through the studios—

Ooh, they sell long sausages in buns!

Anyone else want a long sausage in a bun?

Uh, yeah, I'll have one.

Yes, please, McBoo.

Actually, me too, yeah.

We ended up with...

Oh, look at the time. We'd better go in.

SCREEN

TICKET OFFICE

63

Hello, sir. What can I get you?

Four long sausages in buns, please.

Four long sausages in buns coming right up!

Anything on them? Mustard? Ketchup?

Everything!

Well, okay! I can see you are a gentleman of refinement and taste, sir.

So, you were saying...?

Yeah, so we took all the film of—

Here you go, everyone. Long sausages in buns.

Shh! It's starting.

Mmm... long sausages in buns! Lovely!

So you took all the film of me and McBoo chasing Bump in the Lobzilla costume...

...and you made it into a movie?

But it doesn't make any sense at all!

Who could possibly enjoy—

This is **fantastic**!

It's going to be a massive hit, Bergman.

You and McBoo are gonna be huge stars!

Oh no!

You know, they should really think up a snappier name than "long sausages in buns", don't you think?

I've never really given it much thought.

Careful! They're hot!

Talking of names: what's this stupid movie called anyway?

Good Dog, Bad Dog.

Really?

That's a **terrible** title!

Well I like it.

Um, are you going to finish that?

THE END